Stargazers

Description

Beginning with a fascinating biography of astrophysicist Neil deGrasse Tyson, learners are introduced to the beauty of looking up in wonder at the night sky. They explore the phenomenon that stars are visible at night but not during the day using a model. They also observe the phenomenon of constellations moving across the night sky. Finally, they create a lift-the-flap book sharing what they learned about stars.

Alignment With the *Next Generation Science Standards*

Performance Expectation

1-ESS1-1: Use observations of the Sun, Moon, and stars to describe patterns that can be predicted.

Science and Engineering Practices	Disciplinary Core Idea	Crosscutting Concept
Asking Questions and Defining Problems Ask questions based on observations to find more information about the natural and/or designed worlds. **Analyzing and Interpreting Data** Use observations (firsthand or from media) to describe patterns and/or relationships in the natural and designed world in order to answer scientific questions and solve problems. **Obtaining, Evaluating, and Communicating Information** Read grade-appropriate texts and/or use media to obtain scientific and/or technical information to determine patterns in and/or evidence about the natural and designed world(s).	**ESS1.A: The Universe and Its Stars** Patterns of the motion of the Sun, Moon, and stars in the sky can be observed, described, and predicted.	**Patterns** Patterns in the natural world can be observed, used to describe phenomena, and used as evidence.

Note: The activities in this lesson will help students move toward the performance expectations listed, which is the goal after multiple activities. However, the activities will not by themselves be sufficient to reach the performance expectations.

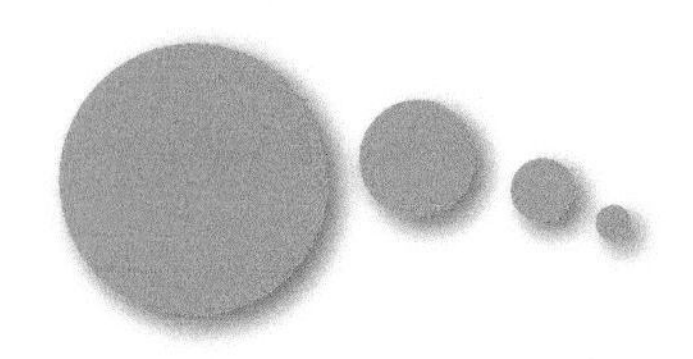

Featured Picture Books

TITLE: ***Look Up With Me: Neil deGrasse Tyson: A Life Among the Stars***
AUTHOR: **Jennifer Berne**
ILLUSTRATOR: **Lorraine Nam**
PUBLISHER: **HarperCollins**
YEAR: **2019**
GENRE: **Narrative information**
SUMMARY: *Tells the inspiring true story of Neil deGrasse Tyson as he discovers the wonders of space, the thrill of science, and the joy in sharing the beauty of our amazing universe.*

TITLE: ***Jump Into Science: Stars***
AUTHOR: **Steve Tomecek**
ILLUSTRATOR: **Sachiko Yoshikawa**
PUBLISHER: **National Geographic**
YEAR: **2006**
GENRE: **Non-Narrative Information**
SUMMARY: *Introduces stars and what they are made of, how they shine, why you can only see them at night, and more.*

Time Needed

This lesson will take several class periods. Suggested scheduling is as follows:

Session 1: **Engage** with *Look Up With Me* Read-Aloud and Neil deGrasse Tyson Video

Session 2: **Explore** with Stargazing Time Lapse Videos and Stars Model

Session 3: **Explain** with *Jump Into Science: Stars* Read-Aloud and Constellations

Session 4: **Elaborate** with Pictures in the Sky

Session 5: **Evaluate** with Stargazers Lift-the-Flap Book

Materials

For Star Model (per student):

- 1 LED keychain flashlight
- Aluminum foil square (approx. 4" × 4")
- Pushpin
- Paper towel tube or cardboard shipping tube of similar size

For teacher use:

- Stargazing app (see "Websites" section)
- Large, bright flashlight
- Canis Major, the Great Dog to project

SAFETY

- Remind students to use caution when working with pushpins (a potential sharp and impalement hazard) to avoid cutting or puncturing skin or eyes.
- Only have students use pushpins under direct adult supervision and then collect the pins.
- Remind students to never look directly at the flashlight.
- Have students wash hands with soap and water after completing activities.

Student Pages

- Pictures in the Sky
- My Constellation
- Stargazers Lift-the-Flap Book
- STEM Everywhere

Background for Teachers

Children are naturally fascinated by objects in the night sky, and stargazing with kids is a great way to nurture an early interest in STEM as well as a sense of wonder about the natural world. This lesson begins with a read-aloud about a man who never outgrew his childhood wonder about the stars and became one of the world's most famous astrophysicists, Neil deGrasse Tyson. Dr. Tyson's affinity for the stars began when he visited the Hayden Planetarium at 9 years old. He attended public school in New York City and eventually went on to study astrophysics at some of the most prestigious universities in the country—Harvard, University of Texas at Austin, Columbia, and Princeton. Dr. Tyson has dedicated his career to sharing the wonders of the universe with others. He is currently the director of the Hayden Planetarium, host of the television show *Cosmos: A Spacetime Odyssey*, and host of a podcast called *Star Talk*. In 2015, he was awarded the Public Welfare Medal from the U.S. National Academy of Sciences for his "extraordinary role in exciting the public about the wonders of science."

The featured book about Neil deGrasse Tyson's life, *Look Up With Me,* highlights his insatiable curiosity and inspires children to look up at the sky with wonder and curiosity themselves. In the absence of light pollution, children can see an ever-changing display of objects in the night sky. These objects may include twinkling stars, non-twinkling planets, constellations, the Moon, "falling stars" or streaks of light caused by burning meteoroids, meteor showers, aircraft, and satellites. Spotting the International Space Station is a special treat—it is the third brightest object in the sky and looks like a very fast-moving plane. You do need to know when and where to look, so check out NASA's Spot the Station website at *https://spotthestation.nasa.gov*.

Young students should be encouraged to draw and talk about what they see and think when they are observing the sky. At the beginning of this lesson, students are invited to observe the night sky with an adult helper. A useful internet resource for stargazing is StarDate, located at *www.stardate.org*. The website includes stargazing tips for beginners, a sky almanac, information on constellations, and much more. Another option for stargazing is to have a star party at which the teachers, students, and parents meet to look at the stars together. This can be held in the schoolyard, an observatory, or a local park. Contact a local astronomy club or observatory center to assist with setting up a star party for your class. At the end of this lesson plan are several stargazing apps that can quickly and easily tell you what you are looking at in the night sky. We have provided video links so you can also have a "star party" in the classroom.

In the *explore* phase of the lesson, students use a model to show that the stars and planets are still there during the day; we just can't see them because our star, the Sun, is so bright. In the *explain* phase of the lesson, students also learn from a nonfiction read-aloud that stars are round, different sizes, and different colors depending on how hot they are, and why we can only see stars at night. The book also introduces the phenomenon of *constellations,* patterns of stars that people have imagined as various figures, animals, or objects. Over thousands of years, many civilizations have tried to explain the patterns of stars in terms of their own cultures. These constellations include such pictures as a bear, a

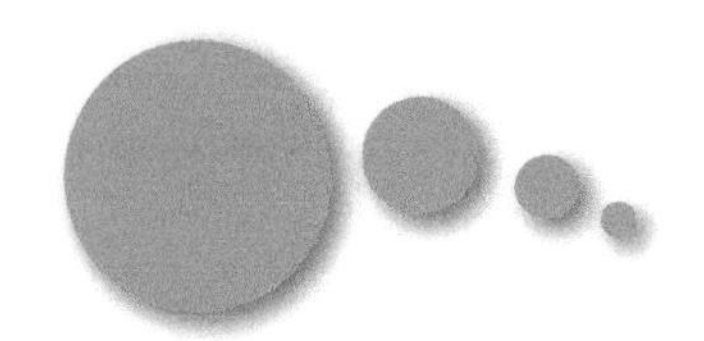

dog, a lion, and a hunter. To try to explain these patterns, people gave them names and made-up stories about them. The International Astronomical Union recognizes 88 constellations. It is important for students to understand that the names and stories behind the constellations were made up in the imaginations of people. The night sky is what we see when our side of Earth faces away from the Sun. Due to Earth's revolution around the Sun, we look out on different parts of the universe at night. This is why we see different constellations at different times of the year.

The crosscutting concept (CCC) of patterns is prominent in this lesson as students observe the pattern that the stars are visible during the night but not during the day. By observing time-lapse videos and listening to a read-aloud, they learn that the stars also follow a pattern as they move across the night sky from east to west as Earth turns. Students engage in the science and engineering practice (SEP) of asking questions and defining problems as they formulate questions based on their observations of the night sky, as well as the SEP of obtaining, evaluating, and communicating information by reading nonfiction books and then creating a lift-the-flap book sharing what they have learned.

In the later grades, students will learn more about how the brightness and distance of stars affects their appearance and further explore the pattern of the apparent motion of the stars across the sky.

Learning Progressions

Below are the disciplinary core idea (DCI) grade band endpoints for grades K–2 and 3–5. These are provided to show how student understanding of the DCIs in this lesson will progress in future grade levels.

DCI	Grades K–2	Grades 3–5
ESS1.A: The Universe and Its Stars	• Patterns of the motion of the Sun, Moon, and stars in the sky can be observed, described, and predicted.	• The Sun is a star that appears larger and brighter than other stars because it is closer. Stars range greatly in their distance from Earth.

Source: Willard, T., ed. 2015. *The NSTA quick-reference guide to the* NGSS: *Elementary school.* Arlington, VA: NSTA Press.

engage

Look Up With Me Read-Aloud

Inferring

Show students the cover of the book *Look Up With Me: Neil deGrasse Tyson: A Life Among the Stars. Ask*

? What do you think this book is about?

? Have you ever heard of Neil deGrasse Tyson?

? If you haven't heard of him, are there any clues about him on the cover or in the title?

Show students the back cover of the book. *Ask*

? Are there any clues about Neil here?

Model how the back cover of the book can often help you find out more about what's inside. Read the text on the back of the book that ends, "the inspiring true tale of Neil's life and how he became a world-famous astrophysicist." Explain that now we know that Neil is a real person and that this is a true story. *Ask*

? What is an astrophysicist? (Answers will vary.)

Let's read and find out!

Connecting to the Common Core
Reading: Informational Text
Key Ideas and Details: 1.1

Read the book aloud. Then *ask*

? So, what is an astrophysicist? (A scientist who studies planets, moons, and stars [page 12 of the book].)

? How did Neil get interested in space? (He took a trip to a planetarium.)

? How did Neil get the money to buy a telescope? (He walked dogs for 50 cents a walk.)

? Have you ever looked into a telescope? (Answers will vary.)

? What other things, besides astrophysics, did Neil like to do? (dance, wrestle, take pictures, and laugh)

? Where does Neil work now? (At the same planetarium where he was first inspired to study space, the Hayden Planetarium in New York City.)

Neil deGrasse Tyson Video

Making Connections: Text to Media

Connecting to the Common Core
Reading: Informational Text
Integration of Knowledge and Ideas: 1.9

Tell students that you have a video of Neil deGrasse Tyson to share so they can see what he looks and sounds like in real life. Ask them to compare and contrast the video to the book they just read about Neil. What's the same? What's different?

Show the 7:21-minute "The Secret Life of Scientists" video (available in the "Websites" section at the end of this lesson). *Note:* the video is divided into five sections.

After watching, *ask*

? What was the same? (The video and book both showed Neil as a kid, included the Hayden Planetarium, showed Neil's telescope, and so on.)

? What was different? (The book explained how he walked dogs to make money to buy a telescope and the video did not; the video showed how Neil has a collection of neckties that are space themed, and so on.)

? How did the book and video together give you a more complete picture of Neil deGrasse Tyson? (In the book, we learned more about his childhood. In the video, we got to see pictures of what he looked like as a kid and were able to see him as an adult and hear his voice.)

Next, tell students that Neil deGrasse Tyson included a note to the reader in the introduction at the beginning of the book. Read the introduction aloud. *Ask*

? How is being a scientist like being a kid, according to Neil deGrasse Tyson? ("Scientists are kids who never lost their natural childhood curiosity about the world.")

Stargazing

Explain that *curiosity* is a strong desire to learn something or figure something out. It involves asking a lot of questions. *Ask*

? Have you ever looked up with curiosity at the night sky? (Answers will vary.)

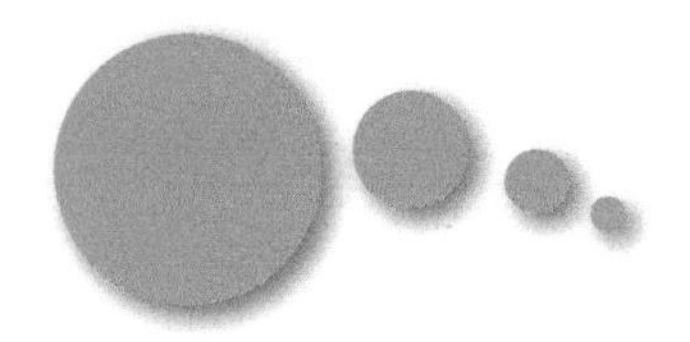

? What can you see in the night sky? (Answers may include stars, planets, clouds, the Moon, and airplanes.)

? What do you wonder about the night sky? (Answers will vary.)

Tell students that you would like for them to look up at the night sky with an adult whenever they have a chance and notice the different objects in the sky. Each day, ask students what they noticed the night before if they were able to stargaze.

explore

Stargazing Time Lapse Videos

Revisit the last two-page spread of *Look Up With Me* that shows the group of people looking up at the stars. *Ask*

? Have you ever heard of a star party? (Answers will vary.)

Explain that a star party is when a group of people get together to look at the stars. They gather in a place that is far away from city lights to get the best view of the stars. They usually bring their telescopes, binoculars, chairs, and blankets. They arrive before it gets dark to set everything up and then wait for the sky to grow dark. Tell students that you are going to have a video star party right here in the classroom. The videos they will see are called time-lapse videos. Explain that a time lapse is video of something that usually happens over a long period of time that is sped up so that you can watch it in a short period of time. The videos they are going to watch were recorded over several hours, but the time lapse allows them to view each one in a minute or less.

CCC: Patterns
Patterns in the natural world can be observed, used to describe phenomena, and used as evidence.

Tell students that as they watch the videos, you would like them to make observations. Show the stargazing videos or similar time-lapse videos of the night sky. (See the "Websites" section for video links.) You may want to show them more than once. Allow students to share observations with a partner as they are watching. After watching, *ask*

? Where do you think the videos were recorded? (near a lake, in a neighborhood, in a city, on a beach, etc.)

? What did you notice? (Students will likely notice that as the sky grows darker, stars appear, the stars seem to move across the sky, streaks of light go across the sky, and you can't see the stars when it turns to day.)

? What pattern of motion did you see? (The stars seem to move across the sky all in the same direction in every video.)

? What do you wonder? (Answers will vary.)

Stars Model

Use students' curiosity about stars to help navigate to the next part of the lesson. *Ask*

? Why can't we see stars during the day? (Answers will vary.)

SEP: Asking Questions and Defining Problems
Ask questions based on observations to find more information about the natural world.

Give students an opportunity to make a mental model by recording their ideas in words and pictures on a piece of paper or sticky note. After they have had a chance to respond to the question individually, have them share their drawings with a partner. Visit pairs and listen to as they explain their ideas.

SEP: Analyzing and Interpreting Data
Use observations to describe patterns in the natural world in order to answer scientific questions and solve problems.

Tell students that they are going to have the opportunity to make a model of the night sky. Give each child materials to build a "starmaker": a paper towel tube or other similarly-sized cardboard tube, a small square of aluminum foil, a pushpin, and a small LED keychain. Have them cover one end of the tube with the foil and poke several small holes in the foil using the pushpin (collect the pushpins as soon as they have done this). Then show them how to place the LED flashlight into the open end of the tube to project "stars" onto the wall. Have everyone shine their "stars" onto the same wall, then turn the classroom lights out so they can be seen clearly. Tell students that the dots of light represent stars at night. *Ask*

? How can we model night turning to day? (Students might suggest turning on the room lights or shining another flashlight.)

Next, hold up a large flashlight and tell students that you are going to use it to represent the sunrise (just like they may have noticed in some of the videos). *Ask*

? What do you think will happen if I shine the bright flashlight on our night sky (wall of stars)? (Answers will vary.)

Turn on the flashlight and slowly move the flashlight beam from the bottom left horizon of your "night sky" upward toward the middle of the "sky." This represents sunrise. *Ask*

? Can you see the stars now? (no)

? Why not? (The Sun—the flashlight—is too bright. We can only see the sunlight.)

Next, slowly move the flashlight beam away from the projected stars until you can see them again. *Ask*

? Can you see the stars now? (yes)

"Starmaker" materials

A "starmaker"

Star model

? So, where did the stars go when the Sun was shining? (They were always there; you just couldn't see them because the Sun was so much brighter.)

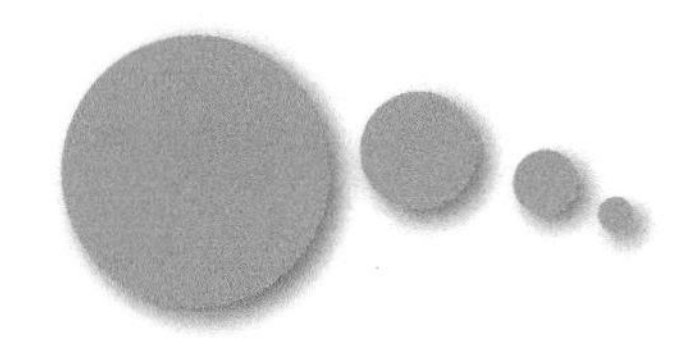

The idea that stars are present during the day but can't be seen in daylight is sometimes hard to comprehend, so another way to prove to students that the stars are still present during the day is to take students outside during the day and use a stargazing app (see the "Websites" section). Point the app at the sky and it will show you which stars and constellations are there.

Using a stargazing app during the day

explain

Have students revisit their drawings to add or revise their thinking. *Ask*

- ? Have your ideas changed?
- ? What did you add to your drawing?
- ? What did you remove from your drawing?

Jump Into Science: Stars Read-Aloud

Show students the cover of the book *Jump Into Science: Stars* and introduce the author, Steve Tomecek. Tell students that you would like them to hear the author's explanation of why we can't see stars during the day and compare it to the explanation they developed.

Determining Importance

> Connecting to the Common Core
> **Reading: Informational Text**
> Key Ideas and Details: 1.1

> **SEP: Obtaining, Evaluating, and Communicating Information**
> Read grade-appropriate texts and/or use media to obtain scientific information to determine patterns in the natural world.

Read pages 1–9 that explain why we can't see stars during the day. *Ask*

- ? Can you see stars easily at night where you live? Why or why not? (Answers will vary.)
- ? Why can't we see stars during the day? (The book says, "The shining sun makes the sky so bright that starlight can't be seen.")
- ? How does this information compare to what we learned using a model? (In our model, the "Sun" [flashlight] made the wall so bright that our "stars" couldn't be seen.)

Next, read pages 10–19 aloud. (You may want to skip pages 14–15 about lightyears as it is abstract and not essential to this lesson.) *Ask*

- ? What are stars made of? (hot, glowing gas)
- ? How was our model different than real stars? (Answers may vary, but be sure to point out that real stars produce their own light from hot, glowing gas, whereas the model is made of light coming from a flashlight.)

Constellations

Revisit pages 20–23 of *Jump Into Science: Stars* about constellations. Explain that people who lived long ago looked at the stars often. Without electric

lights shining everywhere, they were able to see the stars a lot better than we can. They imagined that groups of stars made pictures, kind of like dot-to-dot pictures. These patterns or pictures are called *constellations*. People gave names to the pictures that have been passed on from generation to generation and are still used today. People also made up stories about the constellations. *Ask*

? Have you ever seen the constellation Orion? (Answers will vary.)

? What did the book say is an easy way to find Orion? (Look for the three stars in a row that make up Orion's belt.)

> **CCC: Patterns**
> Patterns in the natural world can be observed, used to describe phenomena, and used as evidence.

Have students rewatch the videos titled "Orion's Belt—Time Lapse of a VERY Clear Sky" and "TIMELAPSE: Orion Rising" and ask them to try to find Orion. Once students find Orion, have them point to Orion and follow the constellation with their finger as the videos play. Reinforce the crosscutting concept of patterns by *asking*

? What is the same in both videos? (The pattern of stars that forms Orion does not change, and it seems to move across the sky.)

Read pages 24 and 25 and point out the pattern of motion of the stars in the pictures. Invite students to follow the star pattern with their fingers as you read the times from the timeline. *Ask*

? How does this illustration compare to the videos we watched of Orion? (Orion moved in the same direction across the sky.)

Read the rest of the book aloud. *Ask*

? What did you learn about stars?

? What are you still wondering about stars?

elaborate

Pictures in the Sky

Pairs Read

Revisit pages 20 and 21 about constellations and remind students that constellations are imagined pictures, just like playing connect the dots with the stars. Pass out the Pictures in the Sky student page, and have pairs read the name of each constellation and its story. Students will probably notice that the shape of each constellation does not look exactly like the person or animal for which it was named. People used a lot of imagination to come up with the names and stories for constellations. Mention that students will not be able to see these constellations on all nights because of Earth's orbit around the Sun.

Writing

> Connecting to the Common Core
> **Production and Distribution of Writing: 1.5**

Next, give students crayons or markers and pass out the My Constellation student page. Invite students to use their imaginations to create their own constellations and stories out of the star pattern on the page.

When students are finished, have them share their constellations with the class. *Ask*

? Why do you think we all have different pictures, names, and stories when we all started with the same pattern of stars? (We all used our own imaginations to make up the pictures, names, and stories.)

Next, project the Canis Major, the Great Dog page. Explain that long ago, the Greeks saw the same pattern of stars in the sky and imagined that it made a picture of a dog. They called this constellation

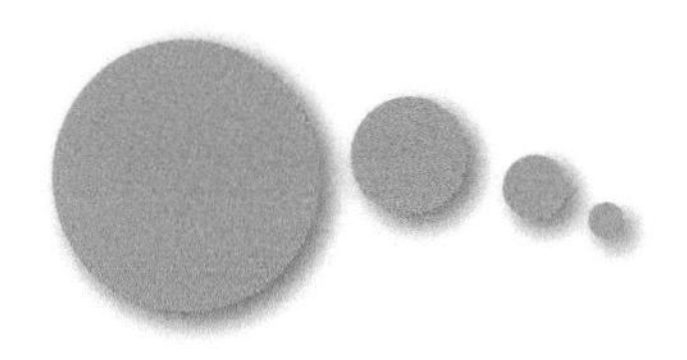

Canis Major, or the Great Dog. Read the brief story of Canis Major on the overhead, and then *ask*

? How does your picture compare to Canis Major?

? Is there one right way to connect the dots and imagine a picture? (No, everyone imagines something different.)

Explain that even though the names, pictures, and stories associated with constellations are all made up, astronomers still use the constellations to find certain stars in the night sky. Tell them that there are 88 constellations that are recognized and used by astronomers. No matter when or where you see these constellations, the stars that form them are always in the same arrangement.

evaluate

Stargazers Lift-the-Flap Book

Writing

> Connecting to the Common Core
> **Writing**
> Research to Build Knowledge: 1.8

Tell students that they are going to have an opportunity to show what they have learned about stars. Give each student a copy of the Stargazers Lift-the-Flap Book student pages. Have them fold each page on the dotted line and then staple the pages together. For each question, students can write and draw their answer.

? What patterns of motion can you see in the sky? (The Sun, Moon, and stars all move in the same direction across the sky.)

Stargazers Lift-the-Flap Book

? Why can't we see stars during the day? (Possible correct answers: The stars are still there. You just can't see them when the Sun is shining. The Sun is too bright.)

? What are constellations? (Possible correct answers: patterns of stars that make imaginary pictures; pictures people imagine from connecting the dots of stars)

STEM Everywhere

Give students the STEM Everywhere student page as a way to involve their families and extend their learning. They can do the activity with an adult helper and share their results with the class. If students do not have access to the internet at home, you could print and copy the Stargazing page for the week from the StarDate website.

Opportunities for Differentiated Instruction

This box lists questions and challenges related to the lesson that students may select to research, investigate, or innovate. Students may also use the questions as examples to help them generate their own questions. These questions can help you move your students from the teacher-directed investigation to engaging in the science and engineering practices in a more student-directed format.

Extra Support

For students who are struggling to meet the lesson objectives, provide a question and guide them in the process of collecting research or helping them design procedures or solutions.

Extensions

For students with high interest or who have already met the lesson objectives, have them choose a question (or pose their own question), conduct their own research, and design their own procedures or solutions.

After selecting one of the questions in this box or formulating their own questions, students can individually or collaboratively make predictions, design investigations or surveys to test their predictions, collect evidence, devise explanations, design solutions, or examine related resources. They can communicate their findings through a science notebook, at a poster session or gallery walk, or by producing a media project.

Research

Have students brainstorm researchable questions:

? What constellations can you see in the summer? In the winter?

? What is the closest star to Earth besides the Sun?

? What are some constellations other than the ones mentioned in the lesson?

Investigate

Have students brainstorm testable questions to be solved through science or math:

? Can you use a stargazing app to locate planets in our solar system?

? About how many stars can you see on a given night from your neighborhood?

? Do constellations look different at different times of night?

Innovate

Have students brainstorm problems to be solved through engineering:

? Can you design a stargazing pack tto organize and carry all of your supplies?

? Can you create a model of our solar system?

? Can you find out how to build a DIY telescope?

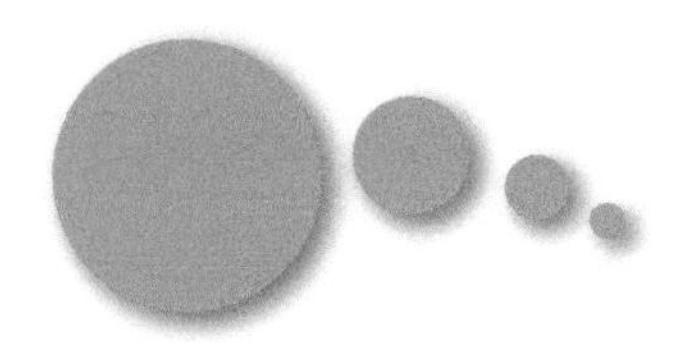

Websites

The Secret Life of Scientists: Neil deGrasse Tyson from PBS
www.pbs.org/video/secret-life-of-scientists-neil-degrasse-tyson-astrophysicist

StarDate Website from the McDonald Observatory
https://stardate.org

Stargazing Time Lapse Videos

Dark Skies at Assateague Island National Seashore—4K Timelapse
www.youtube.com/watch?v=sB8Jocv7A1Q

Gorgeous 360 8K Timelapse of the Milky Way Rising Over the Sonoran Desert
www.youtube.com/watch?v=eq2jM7oJD1c

Orion's Belt—Time Lapse of a VERY Clear Sky
www.youtube.com/watch?v=x0i32cMacXI

TIMELAPSE: Orion Rising
www.youtube.com/watch?v=tB1zjYMhbtg

Stargazing Apps

Star Walk App

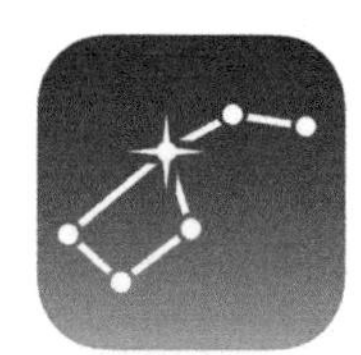

Night Sky App

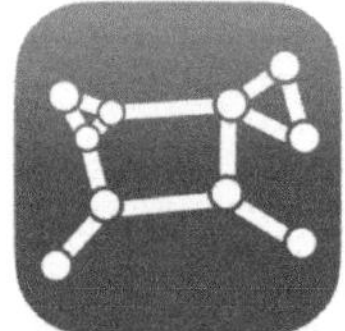

Pocket Universe App

More Books to Read

Ahmed, R. 2021. *Mae among the stars.* New York: Scholastic.
Summary: This true story of Mae Jemison, the first African American woman to travel in space, will inspire other young people to reach for the stars.

Asch, F. 2000. *The Sun is my favorite star.* New York: Gulliver Books, Harcourt.
Summary: This book celebrates a child's love of the Sun and the wondrous ways in which it helps Earth and the life upon it.

Branley, F. M. 1991. *The big dipper.* New York: HarperTrophy.
Summary: This Let's-Read-and-Find-Out-Science book explains basic facts about the Big Dipper, including which stars make up the constellation, how its position changes in the sky, and how it points to the North Star.

Branley, F. M. 1983. *The sky is full of stars.* New York, HarperTrophy.
Summary: This Let's-Read-and-Find-Out-Science book explains how to view stars and ways to locate star pictures, known as constellations, throughout the year.

Drimmer, S. 2017. *National Geographic readers: Night sky.* Washington, DC: National Geographic Kids.
Summary: Simple text and appealing photographs reveal the features of the night sky.

Rau, D. M. 2005. *Spots of light: A book about stars.* Mankato, MN: Picture Window Books.
Summary: From the Amazing Science series, this book provides a simple introduction to stars.

Soltis, S. 2020. *The stars just up the street.* Somerville, MA: Candlewick Press.
Summary: When Mabel's grandfather was a child, he could see thousands of stars from his backyard. Mabel figures out what she needs to do in order for her and her neighbors to see a sky full of stars.

Thacher, M. 2020. *Sky gazing: A guide to the Moon, Sun, planets, stars, eclipses, and constellations.* North Adams, MA: Storey Publishing.
Summary: This detailed guide to the night sky is a great resource for enthusiastic young stargazers.

Pictures in the Sky

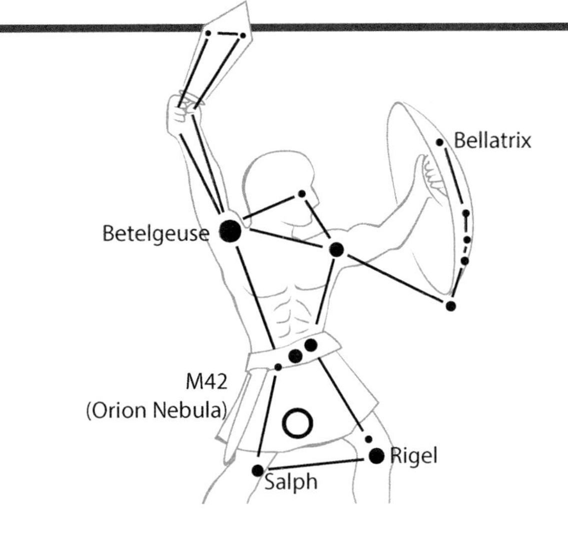

Orion, the Hunter
Orion is a hunter who roams the forest with his dog.

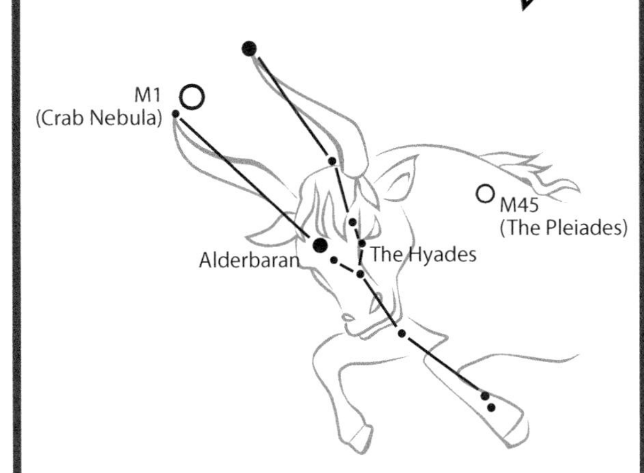

Taurus, the Bull
Taurus is a white bull who flies across the night sky.

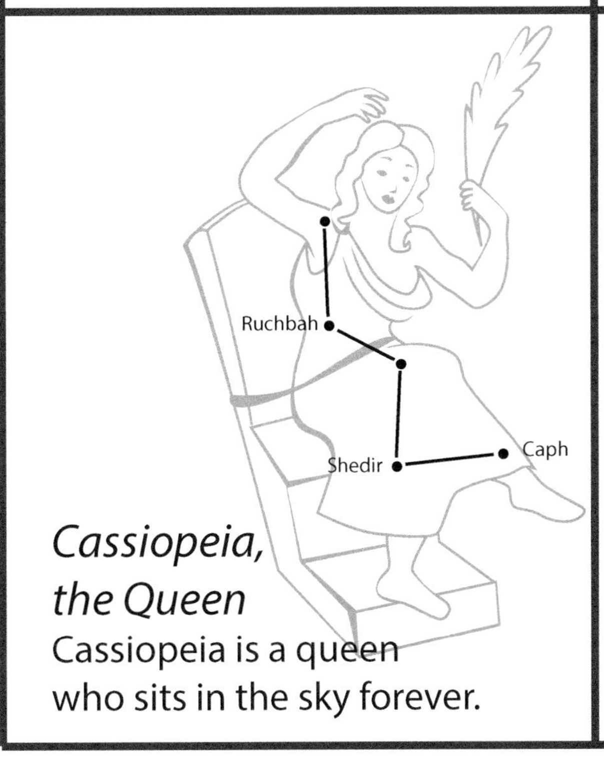

Cassiopeia, the Queen
Cassiopeia is a queen who sits in the sky forever.

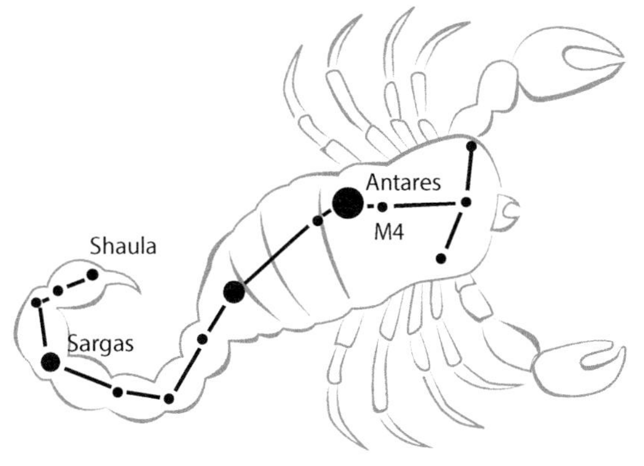

Scorpius, The Scorpion
Scorpius is a scorpion who stung Orion on the foot.

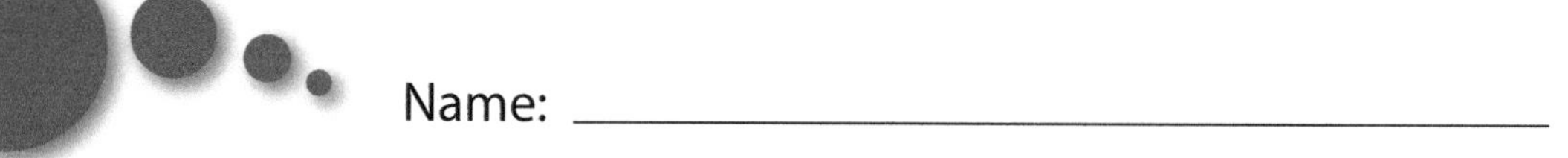

Name: ______________________________

My Constellation

Use your imagination to create a picture out of the pattern of stars below. Choose a name for your constellation and write a story about it.

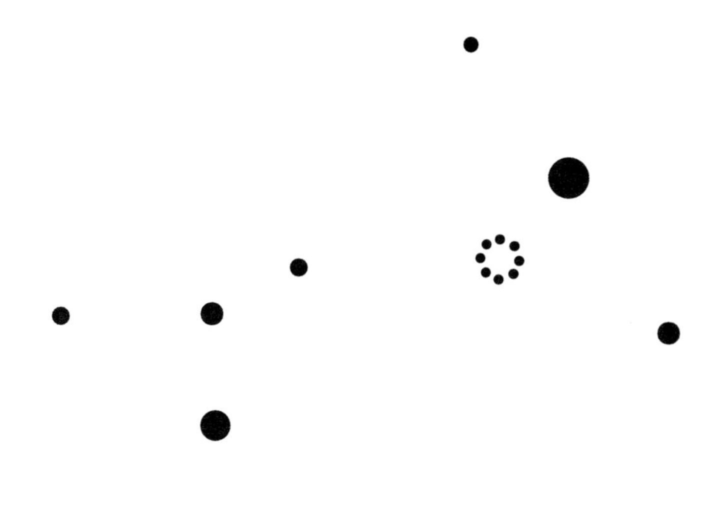

Name of My Constellation: ______________________________

The Story of My Constellation:

____

____

____

Canis Major, the Great Dog

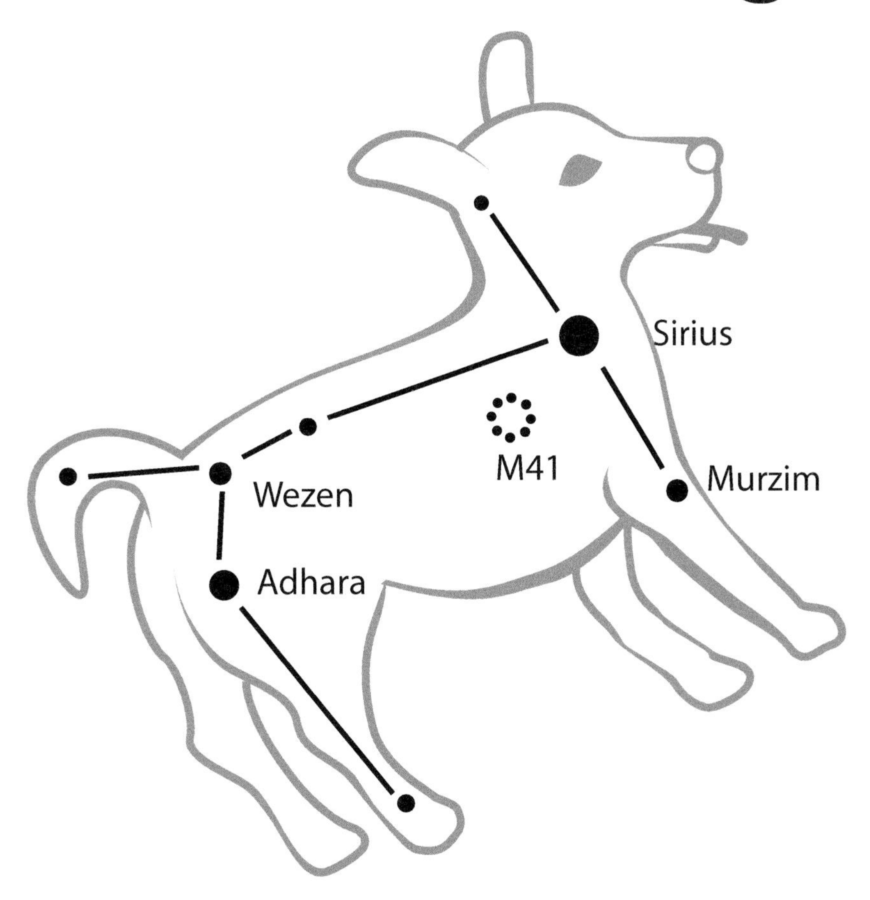

The Story of Canis Major

The Great Dog belongs to Orion the hunter. He follows his master across the sky, forever chasing Lepus, the rabbit. Canis Major could run incredibly fast. He won a race against a fox that was the fastest creature in the world. The dog was placed in the sky to celebrate the victory.

Stargazers

Lift-the-Flap Book

by ______________

What patterns of motion can you see in the sky?

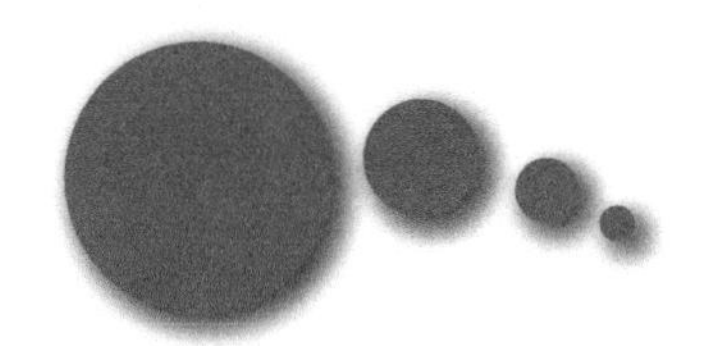

Why can't we see stars during the day?

What are constellations?

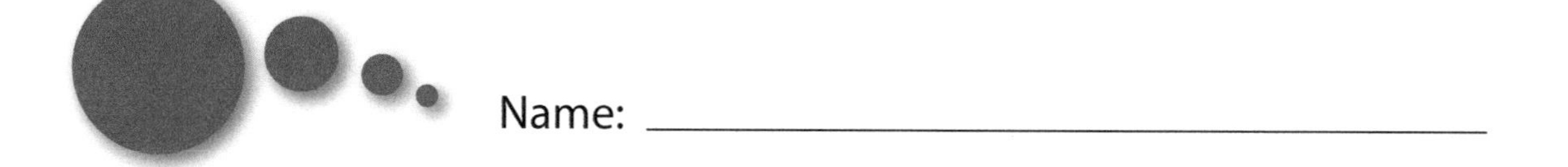

Name: ______________________________

STEM Everywhere

Dear Families,

At school, we have been learning about **stars.** We learned that stars are only visible at night, except our daytime star, the Sun. We learned that **constellations** are patterns and pictures in the stars that people imagined long ago when they "connected the dots," and even though the pictures are imagined, astronomers still use constellations to describe the locations of stars in the sky. To find out more, ask your learner the following questions and discuss their answers:

- What did you learn?
- What was your favorite part of the lesson?
- What are you still wondering?

At home, you can visit the McDonald Observatory website to see what to look for this week in the night sky. Scan the QR code or go to *https://stardate.org/nightsky* to find dates and descriptions of objects that will be visible (without a telescope) this week. Then go outside with your learner and see if you can find these objects. Together, draw and write what you saw below.